How Not to Date Online
(with One Boob)

by Jo Turner

Published by JJ Moffs Independent Book Publisher 2019

JJ Moffs Independent Book Publisher Ltd
Grove House Farm, Grovewood Road,
Misterton, Nottinghamshire DN10 4EF

ISBN 978-0-9957881-1-4

Printed and bound in Great Britain by Clays Ltd, Elcograf S.p.A
Typeset by Anna Richards
Cover and illustrations by Emily Addlesee

Turn your face towards the sun,
let the shadows fall behind you.
Don't look back, just carry on
and the shadows will never find you.

Walt Whitman

Dedicated to all the single women of 2019;
two boobs, one boob, no boobs, we've got this!

Knowledge is power!

 x

PART 1 - THE JOURNEY

September 2014

A normal day in the office. It had been quite warm for the past few weeks, so I was wearing sleeveless dresses for work. My left armpit had been so itchy for a few weeks, but this week it was getting really irritating.

'That's the third time you've had to go wash your armpit in the sink today, Jo,' said a colleague.

Oh great someone's noticed, I thought. I mean, I'd only worked there a year and now I was going to be known as the "armpit washer" amongst the staff. Brill! Maybe it was the hot weather or the time of the month. I didn't think much of it then, it was just an irritability.

Moving house with a one year old daughter had caused more stress than planning a wedding day or having a baby ever could. So one October evening, as I lay in the luxury of a hot bath in my new dream house with my daughter sound asleep in bed, my thoughts stopped suddenly. That's strange I haven't felt that before, I thought as I rubbed my fingertips against a hard pea sized lump in my left breast. I must be due on my period. I felt it again; the lump was still there. Over the next two weeks, I spoke to friends about it in passing. After all, being only 26 years old, I had no idea what it was or what to do about it, although I knew something wasn't quite right.

17th October 2014

As I was flicking through the TV channels, I lingered on a programme with a statistic that said one in every three would get cancer. I stayed on the channel and watched.

Up next popped the familiar face of Davina McCall. It was a programme I had not seen before called Stand Up to Cancer. Right, that's it, I thought. I need to book an appointment first thing on Monday morning. Running through my head was the knowledge that out of six best friends from school, one had been diagnosed with Cervical Cancer the previous year. So why the hell do I think I won't happen to me? I thought. I was mad with myself. How could I be so naive when my best friend, my bridesmaid, had gone through cancer? Yet here I was still under the impression I was too young to get it!

Fast forward to one week later. I had managed to grab five minutes on my lunch break to ring my doctor.

'I need to come in for a pill review,' I blurted out when the receptionist asked me what I needed an appointment for.

'Are you sure that's all?' the lady asked me.

'Well actually, I have found a lump in my left breast.' I replied meekly.

'Right, let's get you booked in for later today.'

I can actually hear the whole conversation in my head even now.

As I sat on the doctor's couch with my top half exposed, the GP told me she believed it was a cyst so she would give me antibiotics and to come back in a month. Well, probably to the doctor's surprise (and my own), I refused to get dressed until she did something about it. Right now, today! I knew deep down something was seriously not okay.

'Well, I'm going to have to pretend I think it's something more serious if you want me to refer you to the breast suite.'

Little did I know at this point that I didn't fit the 'criteria' to be referred.

'That's fine,' I said 'just do whatever.'

Within three days, I got a letter, and within the first five minutes of the clinical examination at the breast suite, I knew they knew.

So that's when it began. I was the girl with Grade 3, Triple Negative Breast Cancer.

That first appointment with the clinical nurse and the oncologist was indescribable. As I sat next to my mum, a plan was worked out. Research had shown that women of my age bracket and type had a better survival rate if they had chemotherapy before an operation. Also, this plan meant the doctors would be able to get me the genetics test necessary to determine what type of surgery I would need. Who was I to argue? I literally had been plummeted right in at the deep end. In fact, that deep I could have

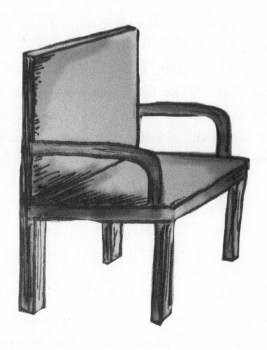

cried with wishing that I could go back to the past months where I was a first-time mum having nothing but sleepless nights to worry about.

'Nine WEEKS?' I blurted out! 'No, I can't wait that long for the chemo to start, I will just feel like I'm sitting for nine weeks waiting to die!'

The oncologist continued the monologue.

'No, I don't care about freezing my eggs. I'm lucky enough to have one healthy child, and she needs a mum.'

What was happening to me? Why had I got turrets all of a sudden?! My mum stroked my hand, and the oncologist came back into the room.

'Okay, we can start next Friday.'

For all the do's and don't's which come as part and parcel of chemotherapy, I was going to enjoy a full-fat restaurant cooked meal. My friends and I always joked about, if it came down to it, what would our last meal be? Well, I'll be honest. I felt like I was there and to my surprise, I chose pancakes with bacon and maple syrup (oh and a quick triangle of brie - whoops!).

As I walked into the oncology ward, I was struck straight away by the smell of metal. I walked up to the desk and sat and waited for my name to be called. That morning I had already had the required amount of steroids, but then was given more intravenously. I never thought twice about the steroids. To me, they were what bodybuilders used to make their muscles grow quicker. Well, Fuck Me! Didn't that come back to bite me in the bum!

Two hours after leaving the hospital, and my first steroid injection and chemotherapy, I was back.

'Get me in that wheelchair, my legs aren't attached to my body.'

I was apparently shouting at a nurse. They wheeled me straight into a bay in A&E where I took it upon myself to go and climb into an old man's bed, whilst he popped off to the toilet.

'I'm sat on his hat, why am I sat on an old man's hat?'

The nurse calmed me down and laid me back into bed.

'Fuck me, I need to have sex! I need to have sex now!

The nurses at the reception bay were trying not to laugh.

'I'm not joking, I will shit this bed!

That went on, I'm told, for around six hours until a bed became available for me on the oncology ward. Dear God, do I pray for the grace of not being able to remember that!

However, a few hours later, I was laid in the hospital bed, my whole body was shaking, and I was unable to open my mouth to speak. What the hell is wrong with me? I'm dying, I must be dying, I thought. The ward nurse came in to see me in the early hours of the morning.

'It's okay dear, I'm here. I've spoken to the doctors, and we think you've had a bad reaction to the steroids. We think you've had an episode of steroid-induced psychosis.'

So there it is; the epic of epic bites in the bum!

I spent the next five days at home, laid on my bed

having to be fed, and a glass of water with a straw put to my mouth to drink. Apparently, it's what's known as the come-down and shock to my body of what it had been through. Needless to say, steroids were definitely not in my treatment plan anymore.

The side effects from the chemotherapy were beyond anything imaginable. I lost my hair, yes, but the tiredness, the sickness and the mental torture were so unforgiving that some days all rolled into one. I would try and attend a baby singing group every week with my daughter, and I used any spare energy I had to walk across the room to her when she called 'mummy'. I knew I could only walk those minimal steps once that day. The next six months passed so so slowly. Numerous hospital stays, days of sleeping, vomiting and not being able to wash myself. What had I become?

Three weeks later, I was sat back in the oncologist's room.

'What do you mean my genetics test never got sent off?' How could this have happened? My mum and I had asked continuously how the test was going. It needed to be done. I looked at my mum and I could see the sadness creeping in through her eyes. Mum looked at the doctor.

'But she needed the test so she can begin the next part of treatment; her surgery,' she said.

Fast forward and numerous phone calls later, I was fucked. The surgeon wouldn't go ahead without my

genetics test as they needed to know whether to remove one or both breasts and to go private was going to cost £1,500.

Well, bugger me, I hadn't been through the last six months to put myself at risk by waiting for the surgery. To go private meant I would receive the results back within days, and my operation date could still go ahead.

My friends; what I would have done without them? We set up a sponsored walk which, for me at the time, was a big feat. A mere three miles there and back and only 30 feet above sea level, but, trust me, that was enough after finishing chemo two weeks previously. The money was raised, and the genetics test was done. Thankfully it showed I wasn't a BRCA carrier. My daughter was not at risk, and I could crack on with this surgery and get back to the plan.

'Woah, Woah, Woah! No, I don't want a lumpectomy. I need a full mastectomy.'

'But we don't think that in your position and at your age, you can make that life-changing decision of not having a breast for the rest of your life.'

Seriously? Let's just take a minute here: I am 27 years old; I've lived independently since I was 18, I have been to university and got a degree, I am married, I have bought my first house, and I have a two year old child. Under what circumstance can I not make this 'life-changing decision'? Wait. Let me rephrase that. MY life changing decision? Whatever, I thought. I just can't be bothered to fight anymore. I need the surgery to get rid of any last traces of the tumour.

One lumpectomy completed and cancer still found in the margins. A second lumpectomy needed with liposuction of the stomach to fill in the ever gaping hole in my left breast. Again, more cancer found in the margins of the removed breast tissue.

'We'll have to do a mastectomy now,' they said.

'That's fine, crack on.'

What we all believed to be my last operation was to be a left mastectomy with reconstruction from the muscle in my stomach. The next three days were a bit of a blur. I had the nine hour operation and reconstruction, but here I was 36 hours later, being told it hadn't worked properly, and I had a blood clot in my left reconstructed breast. The on-call surgeon came into my room on the ward.

'The operating theatre is full, but we need to get that blood clot out asap.'

So in trundled two nurses and the on-call surgeon began to cut open my left reconstructed breast whilst one nurse used the vacuum to suck excess blood away, and the other stood at the end of the bed to comfort me. I eventually went back into theatre around 8pm that night and woke up again in that same room on the ward at 1am, alone.

The on-duty nurse came into my room. I went to

scratch my right ear with my left hand. There was just a gap where my breast once was.

'I haven't got a boob anymore, have I?' I asked the nurse quietly.

'Just go back to sleep, my love, and the doctor will come round in the morning to talk to you.'

'Fuck it.' That's all that went through my head, and I went back to sleep.

The next morning dawned, and it was from there that I knew I wanted to tell anyone who would listen that breast cancer can happen to anyone, at any age.

I was lucky enough to be asked to be part of a Coppafeel! Breast Cancer Awareness campaign for The Sun newspaper. This was the first time I'd met a bunch of ladies who had also been through breast cancer and had one boob, too. There I was at 27 years old, splashed across a double page with one boob. The amount of response from other women from all over the world was nothing short of amazing. Women were thanking me for talking about the subject and showing my 'abnormal' body as they had been through the same or knew someone that had. The best thing to come from the article was when I was messaged through social media to say a 24 year old woman from Spain had read the article and how to check your breasts. Luckily this spurred her on to do her own check, and she had found a lump which she had caught in time. This is what I had done it for.

Six months of chemotherapy, five days of steroid-induced schizophrenia, weekly counselling sessions, two lumpectomies, one liposuction of the stomach to replace fat loss in the breast, one mastectomy, one reconstruction, one blood clot, one removal of reconstruction, two blood transfusions, six more weeks of chemotherapy, 18 radiotherapy sessions, two hair losses, one house move and one divorce, and here I am.

I thought probably best not to use the above as my bio for my dating app! Maybe I'll leave that part for if the conversation needs a boost?

If I told you the truth

If I told you the truth, would you stay calm?
Would you look into my eyes and hold my damp palms?
As I hold you tight, I can hear your heartbeat,
The blood rushing straight through my body to my feet.
It's starting up now, the time has come,
The machine is buzzing, what am I about to become?
It starts slow and begins to spread,
A new poison you now must not dread.
All you've learnt disappears and this liquid you now should
trust,
They've told you it's for the best so you really must.
My legs turn to jelly, my stomach starts to rock,
The sickness begins and goes all over my new frock.
Stay on repeat for four hours, drip by drip,
biding your time before the machine goes blip.
It's time to go home now back to my house full of
flowers.
Flowers from when friends grieved for what may be,
But I will come back fighting you just wait and see.
The pattern mundane, the hurt, the pain,
Week after week, it just stays the same.

A lump I had found

Back in August 2015 straight after tea,
My husband ran a bath for me.
It's been a long day, your daughter's in bed,
Go along and rest your head.
After a while I started to get clean,
deep conditioner my hair will gleam.
My right hand began to rest
on the front area of my left breast.
What's that I thought,
a lump I had found,
So I lay still thinking maybe it's nothing,
my period's coming around.
The next week appeared and I caught a glimpse in the
mirror,
Has my breast changed or have I just got thinner?
I had just had a baby all sorts can happen,
Blimey, last year my thighs had a gap in them.
You're 26, what on earth can be wrong?
Then Davina McCall told me about her sister strong.
One in three that can't be right,
but it was what I needed to give me the fight.
As I was dismissed by the doctors, I held my own,
For little did I know how my tumour had grown.
An initial assessment in the clinic told me,
For my future was there and all that was to be.
A steroid reaction left me in despair,
Then the following week I lost my hair.
The depression and the tense,

Not at one point did any of this make sense,
Fast forward six months so tired and sick,
The next four operations would repair me brick by brick.
It was not enough that the cancer had dispersed,
Another four months of chemo, I must be cursed.
Reaction after reaction no more could I walk,
The times I could eat, I could not use a fork.
My muscles were weary my nerves were shot,
Another four weeks to go, that's all I've got.
Four more weeks of radiation,
I can tell you this sun was not like any type of vacation.
It's now Christmas Eve 2016,
It's time to forget all that I've seen.
'You're fine now' crack on, go live your life,
The strings were cut as sharp as a knife.
You live your life like a game of roulette,
So take your chances, place your bet.
I try to live life with courage in my heart,
But as soon as you feel a twinge, it's like you've been shot with a dart.
But this chapter must close, I've learnt you can look back,
But only as a reminder and a pat on the back.

Iceland Trek 2016

Eight months post cancer treatment.

Initially I booked this to have something to look forward to and, realistically, to prove to myself I was still alive and could achieve anything I set my mind to.

From the age of 19 years of age, I had suffered from quite severe anxiety after my mum was diagnosed with ovarian cancer. I had panic attack after panic attack. At my worst, I couldn't even go to my local food shop. I would panic whilst in the queue at the till, and have to make an excuse and leave my shopping on the conveyor belt, with the lady on the till looking at me like I was slightly crazy.

Well, for the next five years I kind of felt like it. Someone once said to me when you have a panic attack, it's hard to go back to a time when they weren't part of your life. For me, that was totally true. It restricted my life educationally whilst I was at university and also my social life as I couldn't bear to leave the house.

So, being diagnosed with breast cancer at 26, you would think everything would have gone tenfold, and my anxiety would have been out of control. Well, for part of it, that is true. During my treatment, I felt all the emotions of anxiety and panic. However, once my treatment had finished, it was like I had a new lease of life, and I was able to go do all the things I now knew I wanted to do before I died.

So in true illness spirit, I wrote my bucket list:

Number 1 - Go to Iceland.

So obviously, when I saw the advertisement from Coppafeel! I knew straight away I had to apply and would love to try and raise some money for this amazing charity.

So that done, off I went! Quick train trip to Heathrow airport and plane journey with another 60 fabulous people and we were in Iceland.

Split into two teams with our strong women team leaders Vicky Pattison and Chloe Madley we set off. Over three days we were to trek 63k and climb up to 4,500ft; we crossed snow, soil and rocks, freezing water, gorges and we abseiled.

I know the saying is bandied around, but I honestly cannot put into words the experience I had. From start to finish, it really was a physical and mental battle. The one

and only Kris Hallenga, co-founder of Coppafeel was also on the trek; herself and a few others were still on some sort of cancer related treatment. How these inspirational people shaped my life and still do.

As part of the trek, I had the opportunity to stay on for a little longer, where I got to explore the more main attractions of Iceland. So on the 5th morning in Iceland, I got up and went to see the geysers. It was one of the most beautiful and incredible things I have ever seen. As I sat and waited for the tour bus back to the hostel, the whole experience just overwhelmed me and the thought of everything I had come through suddenly grabbed hold of me. I reached into my bag and dug out a postcard I had bought earlier that day to send to my parents. I suddenly found I was able to express all of the emotions I had been feeling, so I began to write a letter to my parents to thank them for supporting me, but also in case the forthcoming scan was not the news that we hoped for.

PART 2

How not to date online...
...with one boob

The struggles of online dating are real. After being diagnosed with breast cancer at the age of 26, divorced at 28 and living as a single parent with one boob, I decided I needed to up my dating game.

So come and join me in the world of dating apps, single men and downright crudeness as we venture into the lessons of how not to date online!

Happy-go-lucky

Oh my God, she's so happy-go-lucky,
Wait, hold on, is that not what you say to a new puppy?!
I might now have one boob, no brows or hair,
But come on folks please do not stare.
I don't want to be the girl that people double take,
I've got breast cancer, now give me a break.
I still want to be sexy, fit and lean,
Back to the time when all the boys were keen.
Now they just want a hug and a few winks,
Is it not enough that cancers stinks?
Well fuck you, you're too tall,
Me and my non-boob will face you all!

Online Dating

Jo, 29yrs

Wanna be comedian
Likes wine
Like adventures
Dislikes Cats
Dislikes vain men
Feel free to talk, however, I'm looking for
more than a new pen pal.

It's a Match!

You and Dan have liked each other.

Dan, 24yrs

Lawyer, Rock climber, Gym enthusiast

---

hey

hi Dan, so you like rock climbing?

yeah, I'm all about the adventure

can I just say you really pretty, I don't think I've ever fancied a fat girl before....

Dan, do you know that's the nicest compliment I've had since I shit myself last year in a nightclub, and my mate told me my hair still looked on point?

This user can no longer be contacted.

It's a Match!

You and Colin have liked each other.

Colin, 39yrs

Warehouse Operative, Keen bird observer,
Keen Gardener

---

hi, I see in your pics you have suffered from alopecia......

No, no, Colin, I've had cancer.

This user can no longer be contacted.

It's a Match!

You and Alan have liked each other.

Alan, 23yrs

Love to travel, Need a co-pilot, Love life

Nice trunk!

thanks it was a bit cold that day, too

I actually meant the elephant but......

This user can no longer be contacted.

It's a Match!

You and Phil have liked each other.

Phil, 37yrs

Party starter, Shot drinker, Ladies' man

Show us ya boobs

you mean boob

no I mean send us a pic of your boobs

yes, I know what you mean, Phil, it's just not plural.

This user can no longer be contacted.

It's a Match!

You and Sam have liked each other.

Sam, 34yrs

Pharmacist, Globe trotter, Women pleaser

So are you going on any holidays soon?

yes, I am actually Australia for three months

Wow! Hope you've been practising your kissing???

LOL, why do they kiss differently there?

Yeah, it's like French kissing but going down under

This user can no longer be contacted.

It's a Match!

You and Barry have liked each other.

Barry, 52yrs

Single, Loves cats, Open minded

I hope you'll take a chance on me, my names Barry, I'm 52, divorced and got severe epilepsy. I'm told I'm a genuine guy; however, I do have a few quirks about me. I've half a big toe, like an orgy and have a penis that won't grow......

You blocked this user.

It's a Match!

You and Courtney have liked each other.

Courtney, 30yrs

Civil Engineer, 5ft 11, Average Build
Looking for a girl younger than me

---

hey x

Hey are you a dwarf? LOL

sorry that sounds bad LOL, I mean are you really small?

is this a serious question?

on what basis have you decided I'm a dwarf???

yes, it's a serious question, it doesn't matter if you are …………

well I'm 5ft 4 Courtney, so I don't think that qualifies me for any dwarf comps no that's not small

unless it's 'the tallest dwarf' comp, cause then I've smashed it!

The following day just continued with what I can only imagine can be classed as an unhealthy fetish for people of a smaller height.

After the monotonous back and forth of what were questionably PC conversations, I requested Courtney tell me his funniest joke.........

I bet you've had more darts out the back of you than snow white.

^ dwarfs

yeah the correct spelling doesn't make it much funnier, to be honest

oh and you're hilarious

well I think it's going well so far, I asked myself and got 100% feedback

This user can no longer be contacted.

It's a Match!

You and Riley have liked each other.

Riley, 21yrs

Hommie, Looking for a peng, Hit me up

What's your whip?

hold on one min

(what's my whip? WHAT IS MY WHIP?)

(SIRI what does my whip mean in slang?)

SIRI – 'A whip has come simply to mean a car.'

so, I ride a totally cool whip

go on........

well I like my cars like I like my men, so I have a very reliable hybrid on the drive.

This user can no longer be contacted.

A whip I mean seriously, who knew this was now the younger generation's chat for my choice of transportation. I mean, if I had been on a date and a lad had asked me that I'd have thought they were simply asking about my desired choice of S&M.

However, after researching this terminology, I think I'm definitely going to use it in my next match.

It's a Match!

You and John have liked each other.

John, 34yrs

Guy next door, Swimmer, Benefits Consultant

It looks like you've not been well on a few of your pics

no, I had to have a mastectomy

wow, I must say how much courage you have for taking that pic

thanks John, that's kind of you

I hope you don't mind me asking but does that mean u qualify for anything else

what, like the Paralympics?

This user can no longer be contacted.

It's a Match!

You and David have liked each other.

David, 42yrs

Lover of life, Floor worker, The real deal

Hey, you got anything planned for Xmas?

just thinking what to get you ....

LOL

want to come look in my big sack......

no thanks David, we'll leave the offer of your bulging scrotum right there.

This user can no longer be contacted.

It's a Match!

You and Darren have liked each other.

Darren, 31yrs

Enjoys magazines (and not the bottom shelf type)

Forgive me Lord for I have sinned it's been 7 days since my last confession

Hmmm ok.....

I looked at your pic & had bad thoughts

Bad??!! As in murder me way or sexual way?

What I wouldn't do to you

Ok, again please clarify, as in drop my body in the river or make love all night?

If I could just kiss you & roll you over

Oh man this is getting a bit deep

Yes it will be so deep

So the river would be deep....?

Will you stop talking about murder while I'm trying to masterbate please

This user can no longer be contacted

It's a Match!

You and Gary have liked each other.

Gary, 28yrs
Self-employed, own house

---

hey you look really beautiful

thanks

how's your day been

oh, yeh really good actually. Thanks for asking

so what are your favourite hobbies?

I loooove good food especially seafood

okay ... right I'm going to take you to the best restaurant in town and get you the best lobster you've ever had

OMG!!! Wait! Is this guy actually normal?! Okay, so quick thought process of pros and cons. ...

Con: he could be an axe murderer (always a con on the top of my list - safety first and all that)
Pro: I get a free meal
Con: I'm worried he looks small on his pics
Pro: he told me his sisters were just really tall
Con: okay I can't think of any more cons I'm just gonna go for it

I'm so excited; it's Thursday night. I'm all dressed up, had a blow-dry and looking forward to meeting a nice guy.

> where shall I meet you?

>> head towards Rotherham

> oh okay

>> then turn left at the petrol station

> yep

>> carry on past the supermarket

> gotcha

>> when you get to the synagogue you've gone too far

> okay I'm on my way

Seriously fuck me! As in ... just help!

I'm sitting in my car, dressed up to the nines,
And there he pulls up in his gas van; it shines.
I don't even want to get out the car,
But I'm just gonna have to go for one drink at the bar.
We got out of our cars and said 'hi' at the step,
He reached over, and our lips met!
His sisters' defo weren't tall, so he lied about his height,
Someone, please help me this is a load of bullshite.
Wait, what is he wearing? Please tell me this is a joke,
A full grey suit and unironed shirt, black loafers, his hair is
gelled slapped to one side, making it look like he's had a
stroke.

I signed up for seafood, a city slicker a tall guy,
But I got a man from Rotherham, a dodgy looking spoons
and a man only 5ft high!
It fair to say I won't be meeting him anymore,
A quick text to my friend; quick, ring me she knows the
score.
'Yes, it's an emergency come home quick.'
Sorry mate I'm gonna have to ditch
He looked so sad with his button hanging on by the last
stitch.
I got out of there as fast as can be,
I'm never dating again well definitely not with a he!

Lesbianism

After a year and a half, I begin to contemplate lesbianism…
now don't get me wrong, I know that it's not a life choice;
we are all just how we are. However, it was still another
27 minutes until the second half of Coronation Street, so I
decided to go ahead with some pros & cons.

Pro: We could have girly dates and go out for food and
cocktails

Con: I couldn't date a vegan (that said I'm not sure in 2019
it's okay to presume all lesbians are vegan?)

Pro: No leaving the toilet lid up

Con: I would have no one to shout at for leaving the lid up

Pro: The house would be tidier

Con: That's means I would definitely have to employ a
cleaner as I cannot bring myself to become tidy

Pro: My new 'girlfriend' wouldn't care about my boob situ

Con: If I lost my hair again people would automatically
presume I was the 'male' in the relationship (haven't
decided quite how I feel about that yet)

Pro: I could wear more fake tan without anyone complaining
about the 'dog biscuit' smell that comes with fake tan

Con: There would be a possibility that now we would have
two people smelling of the above mentioned 'dog biscuit.'

Pro: I would have a loving partner to apply fake tan to my
back instead of me using my handmade contraption of
an electric toothbrush (turned on) with tanning mitt
hanging over the toothbrush itself. Hmmm I think it's
an even race…

Women you are safe for now!

It's a Match!

You and Lewis have liked each other.

Lewis, 24yrs

Loves any kind of bird

- I can ride a bike & drive a truck, I can run, jump, fight and fuck. Stick with me. I'll show you a good time & you'll never need to worry all will be fine

Ha-ha, how does this differ?

Ha-ha, how does this differ?
A tall, handsome man with muscles that look stiffer.
A Peter Kay sense of humour maybe even the looks,
He tells me a one-liner, and he's got me hooked.
Up a tree or with his pheasant,
in a small hole or in the pub,
He showed me how we could laugh
when he first took me for some grub.
A toy-boy a milf or so I've heard,
He now doesn't need to look for any other bird.

As we know a high statistic of men often exaggerate; be it about height, money, etc.. I'll let you decide which one of his exaggerations fell at the first post!

Hidden

Where's she come from with that guy?
She'll cut a line and bake you an apple pie.
She'll sway her new hair and tray and slay.
There she goes thinking she looks like KK.
She'll go to the bar and get you the best round in by far.
But if you look closer, that's when you'll see;
The anxiety, the hurt, more sadness than can be.
With half a scarred body that clothes can hide,
with a changed outlook and a tummy six inches too wide.
When the time comes, she'll be lots of fun.
But she'll turn off the lights and keep her top on.
For when you take the top away and you bare her soul,
that's when all you'll see is a voyage and a hole.
The battle has ended the tears have been dealt;
the prospect of dying still scares her no doubt.
Her face a mask and a heart so cold,
only on the outside does she look bold.
So please remember the next time she asks you around,
that you're lucky you've met her and you're the one to be
found.

PART 3

EXPRESSION & REFLECTION

Cheer the Fuck Up!

Don't be sad and down
by the things you don't have around.
Look at the living around you;
they're the ones that can astound you.
Don't live by curse or domain,
that's the kind of thing that drives you insane.
Look upon life as time that you need,
after all, you're the one that's been freed.
Freed of the darkness, the curse and the fear,
after all, you still remain here.
So come on, cheer the fuck up, my dear!

The Brighter Side

If blue and green should never be seen,
then why is the grass and sky the most beautiful thing
you've ever seen?
From the darkest days to the sun on your face,
they let you know you set the pace.
The moon, the stars, the cold night air,
the spoon and hugs and the tyre spare.
When you wake up daily to be happier than before,
it's then you realise you never needed more.
In return for this new phase,
you then remember that these are the things that cancer
can't change.

The Beautiful Rays of...

As I lay here under the rays,
I stay calm and relaxed, away from the greys.
The light shines bright,
I close my eyes.
The air stays still,
as if I've got time to kill.
My mind is at war,
my heart falls to the floor.
As voices begin,
the realisation sinks in.
The reason I am here enters my brain,
but I need to remember the life I'm trying to maintain.
How different are these rays,
to back then in previous days.
The sun shone warm,
but then began my storm.
My journey completes,
away from the rays and the heat.
I can now fall back to the space,
where the rays are in the right place.

The Ones We Love

Before I went to the breast clinic, I tried to pre-warn my parents that I kinda knew myself that I had breast cancer. How did I know? I'm not sure, but I'm a massive believer (now even more so) of knowing your own body.

So when the time came that evening to tell my parents, I had half hoped they would have already been expecting the worst.

But I guess, when it's *your* child in a possible life or death situation, can you ever actually contemplate facing the worse?

My mum hugged me, my dad looked at me and I could see his heart sink.

It was so strange; my mum had been diagnosed with cancer when I was 18 years old (not linked to mine in any way), and here I was feeling the other side of it. I can honestly say it's completely different. When it's not you, you don't know how the other person is feeling at every hour or minute. So you worry, endlessly, of course, you do. You worry for the parent, you fear for yourself and how you'd possibly live without one of your parents. But when it's you time just freezes, completely stands still. I think it must have been a good three weeks and one lot of chemotherapy when, all of a sudden, I gasped and woke up to the nightmare I was living.

However, now being a mum myself, I can't physically put into words how overly grateful and, in a strange way, contented that I was that it was happening to me and not my child. I guess that's how it's always been ever since I got my diagnosis.

I fought for myself but above and beyond anything else I fought for my baby girl Ella Mary.

A Parent's Dread

No parents ever want to think they might be the ones to
see their daughter dead.
After all, anyone with kids knows that's all you dread.
You want to see your kids grow strong,
See them through their life, all the rights and wrongs.
But as I sit and tell my parents how it will be,
With my body still in shock, a thought came to me.
Of course I was scared,
and all that knew me would be too, that cared.
But I was sat there so glad it wasn't my girl,
My head a mess and my mind a whirl,
Because of course I'm a parent and I would
Take any pain or fear away from her that I could.
Three generations at least affected by this,
I told you cancer really takes the piss.
It doesn't care for your gender or creed,
It just grabs you until you can hopefully beat it and be
freed.

Ella Mary

Your button nose, and your painted toes,
When you sleep you get so sweaty,
With your hair a mess, you look like a yeti!
It's taken some time for us to find us,
But all throughout you remained my must,
My must to live, my must to try,
My must to carry on, not turn and hide.
All I went through, it was just me and you,
You were always there right by my side.
You rubbed my back when I was sick,
You saw my nerves the ones that wouldn't quit.
Every third Friday mummy had to leave,
Each time by heart did bleed.
But when the next week begun,
We went to play with all your friends
At playgroup and had some fun.
I got to see your first day at nursery, school and Christmas
play,
That is why I went through all that rubbish each day.
You make me smile so hard at your jokes,
You're your mother's child that is no hoax.
Your sarcasm, your wit, you're quick as can be,
I love you, Ella Mary, you mean the world to me.

The Things People Say

Sometimes people say things with the best of intentions, but some phrases you could do without...

'Wanna use one of my boobs?'
'Uhhh! Take some of my tummy fat to make a boob?'
'You really suit a bald head.'
'Do you miss your hair?'
'I just don't know how you can live with one boob. Mine are what make me feel feminine.'

You would be surprised how many times ladies actually do say the latter two to me. So I had a quick reflection on the matter and decided now was the time to answer back....

'Wanna use one of my boobs?'
'No, Susan cause then I'd have two saggy boobs.'

'Uhhh! Take some of my tummy fat to make a boob?'
'But why, Marie, would you want to lose your beautiful tummy that carried your beautiful baby?'

'You really suit a bald head, you've got a lovely shaped skull.'
'Seriously?! I feel like Darren Doors/the image of a space raider crisp. Let's be frank, who has a nice shaped skull, Maura?'

'Do you miss your hair?'
'No, no it's a total dream not having a tiny follicle attached to my shiny 'nice skull'. I think I might stay like this.' I mean, really?

Losing Your Hair

A Point of Contention

Getting rid of your hair by choice.

You can shave your head; yes, you will choose to have no hair, but it will get longer rather quickly and very much the same as before.

Losing your hair through chemo.

You are in a state of complete anxiety, you don't know when it will happen, but you can be sure it will.

You dream about it, you wake up and you start to see handfuls of hair on your pillow. You shower, and you lose your arm, leg, pubic hair. You get dry, you go to your mirror as you apply your moisturiser and the hair from your eyebrows and eyelashes comes lose between your fingertips. Your towel looks like someone has swept up the inside of a hairdressers and placed it in it. You begin to cry, your hair is everywhere, everywhere you walk you begin to leave a trail of it behind you. You need to take control, you go back into the empty bath naked and start to shave your own head. As you get dressed and lay back on your bed, the remaining individual follicles feel like each one is a razor blade. Every head movement you make you feel pain, even the straggling bit of stubble that managed to cling on begins to pull out.

So I have to self reflect. I have to let go. Hair does, and breasts do not in any way, define me as a woman. I guess

I'm lucky enough to have had a childhood where I have the platform to be self-aware; to gain self-esteem and to know that I am more than what I see in the mirror. For this, I will be eternally grateful to my parents.

What makes me, me?

- I love to laugh
- I love to be inspired every day
- I thrive off other people's experiences and thoughts
- I have the ambition to get the most out of life
- I have an open desire not to be afraid
- I learn every day never to judge anyone but more to accept and move on
- I appreciate true friendship and what it really means
- I've learnt to love a lot; trust is scary but to never feel love again would be scarier

Reflection

People often ask, 'How can you still believe in God after all that has happened to you?'

I simply reply, 'If no one was ever in pain or sad, then how would you know that things are good?'

Of course, I've had a shit time, and I wish so much that I had never had cancer. But do I wish that my mindset on life was the same as before? Maybe not. Things are very different for me now, from the most simplest of things, like not being able to wear a low cut top or buying a bra off the peg, to the most funniest/strangest of times when my dear mother (diagnosed with Alzheimer's) decided to take my 'fake boob' (made of wadding) out of my swimsuit on holiday and use it to clean the PVC door at our AirBnB, only for her to rinse it out and for me to later find it placed very strategically between the window handle and pane to dry!

As I've said before, it's strange to say I feel lucky, but I really do. Lucky to live, lucky to breathe and lucky to be able to love.

Check Your Boobs!

You know that game you play when you are in college;
'Would You Rather?'
Would you rather want to lose a leg or a foot? You know,
that game that is so politically incorrect but always gets the
best components of your brain working? Yeah that one.
Well, my life feels a little bit like that;
Would I rather have chemo for six months or die sooner?
Would I rather have one boob or two?
Would I rather keep my ovaries or go into menopause at
26 years old?
Would I rather carry on or give up after the first blast of
poison?
I've always been one who hates hindsight,
*"Well thanks for your afterthought, Barbara, but I'm already
stuck in your dad's best Y fronts with two apples stuffed in the
front because you thought it would be soooooo insta worthy!"*
No, just no. No one needs a Barbara like that in their life.
So instead of playing my 'Would You Rather?' all you
need to remember is one thing……..
**Would you rather get an SMS or an EMAIL to
remind you to check your boobs once a month?**

BOOB CHECK 101

What you can do to get to know your boobs.

1 CHECK REGULARLY

This will help you get to know what's normal for you. You can use any method you're comfortable with, such as lying down in bed, standing in front of a mirror or when you're showering.

2 LOOK & FEEL

Remembering to check all parts of your breast, including your armpits, up to your collarbones and your nipples.

3 IF IN DOUBT, GET IT CHECKED OUT

Early detection is the best form of defence, so if you notice anything unusual for you, get it checked out by your doctor.

TEXT **BOOBS** TO ➡ 70300 FOR OUR **FREE** MONTHLY TEXT REMINDER SERVICE

We'll never use this service to ask you for money, and everything we send you is free. Standard network rates apply for the text you send to sign up.

COPPAFEEL.ORG

CoppaFeel! is a registered charity in England & Wales (1132366) and Scotland (SC045970)

GRAB YOUR
BOOBS!
OR YOUR PECS - GUYS, WE'RE TALKING TO YOU TOO!

Did you know that both men and women can get breast cancer? So get into a habit of regularly checking and be aware of the signs and symptoms below. Ladies - remember that some of these changes may occur naturally with your cycle and can be perfectly normal. But if in doubt, get it checked out...

LOOK
changes in skin texture
e.g. puckering/dimpling

LOOK
swelling in your armpit
or around collar bone

FEEL
lumps and thickening

FEEL
constant, unusual pain in
your breast or armpit

LOOK
nipple discharge

LOOK
a sudden change in size
or shape

LOOK
nipple inversion and
changes in direction

LOOK
a rash or crusting of the
nipple or surrounding area

NEED A REMINDER? TEXT BOOBS TO 70300 FOR A FREE MONTHLY TEXT FROM BOOB HQ

We'll never send you spam or ask you to donate money, you'll just get a friendly reminder to check your boobs, once a month. Standard network rates apply for the text you send to sign up but *every* text we send you is free after that, promise.